Simon Goes to School

A MamaLingua Book

AILEEN PASSARIELLO-MCALEER
& CHRISTIA MADACSI HOFFMAN

This is a MamaLingua Book!
published by MamaLingua, LLC

First MamaLingua Edition, August 2018
Copyright ©2018 by MamaLingua
All rights reserved. Published in the United States by
MamaLingua, Austin, Texas, in 2018.

Information on this edition has been submitted to the
Library of Congress.

Text by Aileen Passariello-McAleer
with Christia Madacsi Hoffman
Concept and design by Christia Madacsi Hoffman
Illustrations from Adobe Stock
Illustration assistance and additional artwork
by Clay Hoffman

For permissions or more information about MamaLingua,
visit Mama-Lingua.com.

Printed in the United States of America
ISBN (original paperback): 978-0-692-13989-9
Also available as an ebook.

Tomorrow I go
to a new school.

My mom says it's
una escuela

for kids to become
bilingual.

Bilingüe means being able to speak,

ball = pelota
balloon = globo
bicycle = bicicleta

write, and think in two languages.

My name is Simon.

Yo hablo inglés...

But soon...

My name is Alexia.

We are friends!

Me llamo Simón. ¡Nosotros somos amigos!

Yo voy a hablar español.

Mi mamá says
being able to speak
español e inglés is a

superpower!

And that all of the kids
will be working together
to have the same

¡superpoder!

But I am afraid
that I won't
entender.

Tengo miedo of
feeling *frustrado!*

But my mom says...

everyone is going to feel
the same way.

And that *juntos*...

we will work as a team.

Besides, you don't even need to *hablar*...

to *jugar* together!

Learn Spanish with Simon!

bilingüe – bilingual
entender – to understand
español – Spanish
escuela – school
frustrado – frustrated (m)
hablar – to speak
inglés – English
jugar – to play
juntos – together
superpoder – superpower
yo – I

Me llamo... – My name is...
¡Nosotros somos amigos! – We are friends.
Tengo miedo... – I am afraid...
Yo hablo... – I speak...
Yo voy a hablar español. – I am going to speak Spanish.

MamaLingua

For more language-learning tools, apps, and inspiration,
visit Mama-Lingua.com.

Made in the USA
San Bernardino, CA
07 January 2020